JN061860

What!!

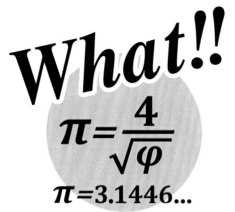

$$\pi = \frac{4}{\sqrt{\varphi}}$$

$\pi = 3.1446...$

Is this true!?

Proposal of a new method for
calculating π available
at the middle school level

Third
edition

Author : Umeniuguisu

BookWay

For all first readers

It may have been better to announce this book at an "academic conference" because of its specialty. However, I didn't or couldn't do so because I am neither a mathematician, scientist nor an engineer of a company. I am just an artisan who engages in manual labor in Japan. However, I am greatly interested in space. I have only a high school level of knowledge about mathematics. You will see that only a middle-school level of mathematics is used in this book when you read it through. I assume quite many people living in Japan can understand this book, including mathematicians, scientists and engineers with an advanced mathematical knowledge, as nine years of education (elementary school and middle school) are compulsory here in Japan. This is why I wrote this book. I wrote this so that readers who know little about mathematics can understand it. If you possess advanced mathematical knowledge, please take note of this.

Aside from those who don't like mathematics, I guess readers of this book will be interested in it substantially. As you can see, this book is not thick. It would be very nice if you could enjoy my proposals on π as a relaxing tea time of math without tackling "difficult problems" wearing a bulldoglike expression.

Author Umeniuguisu

Note: Junior high school students in Japan are 13 to 15 years old.

Table of Contents

Starting with Circle (π) and Five-pointed Star (φ)

Please see the following figure.

You may have seen this figure somewhere. It is a "five-pointed star" inscribed in a circle. Do you know that it has many golden ratios φ (phis)? Only one example is expressed in the figure. The objective of this book is not finding out how many φ (phis) are included in the "five-pointed star inscribed in the circle". If you are interested in this, obtain that knowledge from books or the Internet. Especially, you can obtain a lot of knowledge from the Internet.

I would like to say about this figure that the figure with many golden ratios φ (phis) is beautifully inscribed in the circle. This is one of the greatest reasons for me why I can guess an association between the circle ratio π and the golden ratio φ. From here, I started researching a relationship between π and φ. About four and a half year passed before I started to write this book. It is insignificant as compared to the several-thousand-year history of mathematics, but it felt long to me.

Before going into the main issue, I have another thing to write. I kept to the following three points as I have only a high school level of knowledge about mathematics (my academic major was economics).

1. Using as simple mathematics as possible
2. Not using complex and difficult formula as much as possible
3. Not moving forward when being stuck on calculation

I kept these three points in mind to prevent my brain from getting too confused with mathematics and mathematical formulas. I have another reason for this. Many people know the following formula:

$$E = mc^2$$

It was announced by Albert Einstein. How simple and beautiful it is! A formula describing the circle ratio π and the golden ratio φ would be simple and beautiful like this. This can be imagined from the "five-pointed star inscribed in the circle". I sought to find it out within the scope of my mathematical ability, without trying too hard and collapsing several times. Aside from those who have an advanced mathematical ability, it would be better for readers of this book to question when something is unclear and take a little break before continuing to read it.

Well,　let me go into the main issue.

* The reduction scales of figures in this book are approximate and inaccurate. Please note that this is because I prioritized the visibility of characters, numbers and figures.

Chapter	Finding the Relational Expression
2	**between π (pi) and φ (phi)**

The major issue for me is how I should obtain a relational expression between the circle ratio π (pi) and the golden ratio φ (phi) or find an association chart.

What!? The "five-pointed star inscribed in the circle" already exists?

Of course, I tried to find the relationship between π and φ first using this figure. Using trig functions *sin*, *cos* and *tan* made calculation difficult and confused me, so I gave up. This means that I personally could not find the relational expression with my mathematical ability, not that I deny the possibility of people with advanced mathematical knowledge finding it. I challenged it using other figures, but I gave up. I found a method to find the association in the following figure after much consideration. It is an extension of the process of making φ (phi) using a figure. The figure below shows φ, which you may already know.

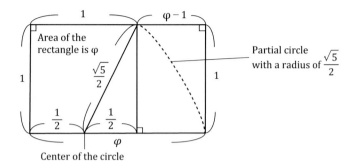

Area of the rectangle is φ

Partial circle with a radius of $\dfrac{\sqrt{5}}{2}$

$\dfrac{\sqrt{5}}{2}$

$\dfrac{1}{2}$ $\dfrac{1}{2}$

φ

Center of the circle

There are some methods to evaluate the value of φ. However, as it is not the objective of this book to describe all of them, I described one I think is easy.

From the figure above,

$$\text{Golden ratio } \varphi \text{ (phi)} = \frac{1+\sqrt{5}}{2} = 1.61803398874\ldots\ldots$$

Then, I provide the following figure to obtain the relational expression between π and φ from the figure above: a "square with the same area" as a rectangle with an area of φ. It is important to make the square.

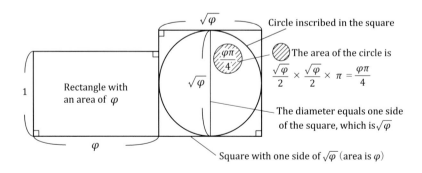

$\sqrt{\varphi}$

Circle inscribed in the square

$\dfrac{\varphi\pi}{4}$

The area of the circle is
$$\frac{\sqrt{\varphi}}{2} \times \frac{\sqrt{\varphi}}{2} \times \pi = \frac{\varphi\pi}{4}$$

Rectangle with an area of φ

$\sqrt{\varphi}$

The diameter equals one side of the square, which is $\sqrt{\varphi}$

φ

Square with one side of $\sqrt{\varphi}$ (area is φ)

8

A value concerning π and φ, $\dfrac{\varphi\pi}{4}$ is obtained. Furthermore, I provide the following similar figure to obtain the relational expression.

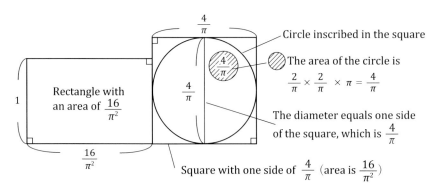

Circle inscribed in the square

The area of the circle is
$$\frac{2}{\pi} \times \frac{2}{\pi} \times \pi = \frac{4}{\pi}$$

The diameter equals one side of the square, which is $\dfrac{4}{\pi}$

Rectangle with an area of $\dfrac{16}{\pi^2}$

Square with one side of $\dfrac{4}{\pi}$ (area is $\dfrac{16}{\pi^2}$)

What! Why is $\dfrac{4}{\pi}$ made?

There are the following three reasons. (I don't describe other reasons in this book to avoid complexity.)

1. The first reason is the value of $\dfrac{4}{\pi}$. Assuming $\pi \approx 3.14$, compare the values of $\sqrt{\varphi}$ and $\dfrac{4}{\pi}$. (* $\approx$ means "nearly equal".)

$$\frac{4}{\pi} \approx 1.27388535031......$$
$$\sqrt{\varphi} = 1.27201964951......$$

The two values are very close. This is the first reason.

2. The second reason is one special feature of $\dfrac{4}{\pi}$. See the following figure and its relational values.

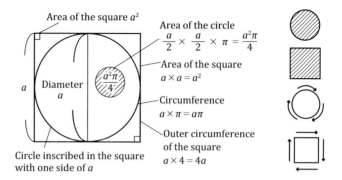

Area of the square a^2

Area of the circle
$$\frac{a}{2} \times \frac{a}{2} \times \pi = \frac{a^2\pi}{4}$$

a Diameter a

$\frac{a^2\pi}{4}$

Area of the square
$$a \times a = a^2$$

Circumference
$$a \times \pi = a\pi$$

Outer circumference
of the square
$$a \times 4 = 4a$$

Circle inscribed in the square
with one side of a

Do you find anything seeing these values?

Multiply the area and circumference of the circle by $\frac{4}{\pi}$.

$$\frac{a^2\pi}{4} \times \frac{4}{\pi} = a^2 \cdots\cdots \text{ This is a value equivalent to the area of the}$$
square.

$$a\pi \times \frac{4}{\pi} = 4a \cdots\cdots \text{ This is a value equivalent to the outer}$$
circumference of the square.

Do you understand? Regardless of the size, values obtained by multiplying the area and circumference of the circle inscribed in a square by $\frac{4}{\pi}$ equal the area and outer circumstance of the square. This is the second reason.

The feature of $\frac{4}{\pi}$ is very helpful for finding out the relationship between the circle ratio π and the golden ratio φ. It can't be found without using it. I recommend you should remember this and use it for subsequent calculations.

3. The third reason is another speciality of $\dfrac{4}{\pi}$.

This speciality will be disclosed later. It is hidden somewhere difficult to find. The speciality was very helpful to guess that $\sqrt{\varphi}$ and $\dfrac{4}{\pi}$ are "exactly the same values", not "very close values".

If you are a curious middle school student, don't cheat and jump ahead! Read this book page by page, as it doesn't have many pages.

Now, I will provide a figure containing one idea to find out the relationship between π and φ.

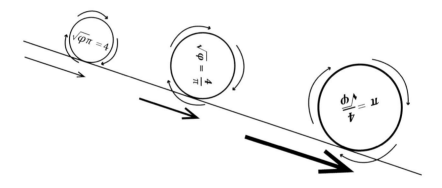

Take a little break!

I have provided the rectangle and square with an area of φ (phi) and those with an area of $\dfrac{16}{\pi^2}$. However, the important formula couldn't be obtained to find out the relationship between π and φ from these figures.

As a result of trial and error, I found that another figure was necessary to find out the relationship between π and φ. It is similar to the two existing figures. However, it is important that it has an unknown x and $\sqrt{\varphi}$ should be set as the area of the circle. The figure is shown below.

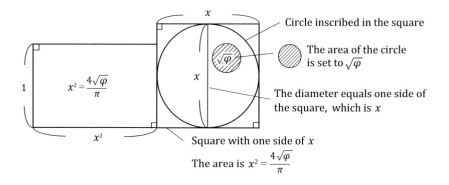

As shown in the figure, "I set $\sqrt{\varphi}$ as the area of the circle intentionally".

What! Why do I $\sqrt{\varphi}$ as the area of the circle?

There are two following reasons.

1. The first reason is the value of $\sqrt{\varphi}$. Compare it with the areas of the circles in the two previous figures. Similarly, I assume π nearly equals ($\approx$) 3.14.

$$\left[\begin{array}{l} \dfrac{\varphi\pi}{4} \approx 1.2701 \ldots\ldots (\text{Area of the circle in the figure with one side of } \sqrt{\varphi}) \\ \dfrac{4}{\pi} \approx 1.2738 \ldots\ldots (\text{Area of the circle in the figure with one side of } \dfrac{4}{\pi}) \end{array}\right.$$

$$\sqrt{\varphi} = 1.2720 \ldots\ldots (\text{Area of the circle in the figure with one side of } x)$$

When the values are compared, you can see they are very close. This is the first reason.

2. The second reason is because setting $\sqrt{\varphi}$ as the area of the circle is a key to evaluate the unknown x and clarify the relationship between the circle ratio π and the golden ratio φ, which is very important. This is highly correlated with the third reason on the previous 11th page, which has a hidden great meaning. Therefore, I would like to unveil it at the end for readers.

For a clearer explanation, I have organized the three figures obtained so far. I assign A, B and C to these figures and a, b, c and d to their qualities.

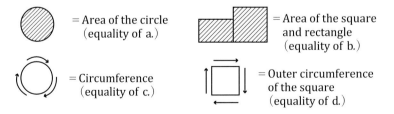

Now, see the organized figures.

Figure A.

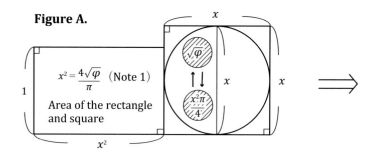

$$x^2 = \frac{4\sqrt{\varphi}}{\pi} \quad \text{(Note 1)}$$

Area of the rectangle and square

Figure B.

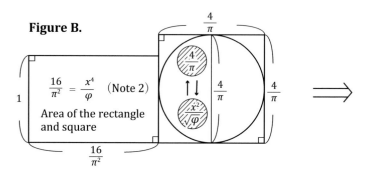

$$\frac{16}{\pi^2} = \frac{x^4}{\varphi} \quad \text{(Note 2)}$$

Area of the rectangle and square

Figure C.

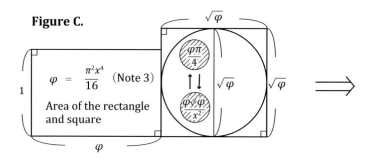

$$\varphi = \frac{\pi^2 x^4}{16} \quad \text{(Note 3)}$$

Area of the rectangle and square

* One side and reduction scales of the figures are approximate and inaccurate.

Note 1: The area of the square (=rectangle) is obtained by multiplying the area of the circle by $\frac{4}{\pi}$.

Note 2: It can be calculated by the equality of B.a.

Note 3: It can be calculated by the equality of B.b.

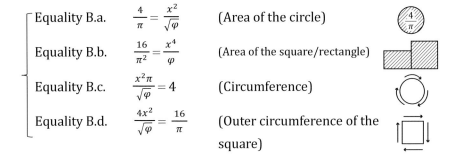

Equality A.a.　$\dfrac{x^2\pi}{4}=\sqrt{\varphi}$　　(Area of the circle)

Equality A.b.　$x^2=\dfrac{4\sqrt{\varphi}}{\pi}$　　(Area of the square/rectangle)

Equality A.c.　$x\pi=\dfrac{4\sqrt{\varphi}}{x}$　　(Circumference)

Equality A.d.　$\dfrac{16\sqrt{\varphi}}{x\pi}=4\,x$　　(Outer circumference of the square)

Equality B.a.　$\dfrac{4}{\pi}=\dfrac{x^2}{\sqrt{\varphi}}$　　(Area of the circle)

Equality B.b.　$\dfrac{16}{\pi^2}=\dfrac{x^4}{\varphi}$　　(Area of the square/rectangle)

Equality B.c.　$\dfrac{x^2\pi}{\sqrt{\varphi}}=4$　　(Circumference)

Equality B.d.　$\dfrac{4x^2}{\sqrt{\varphi}}=\dfrac{16}{\pi}$　　(Outer circumference of the square)

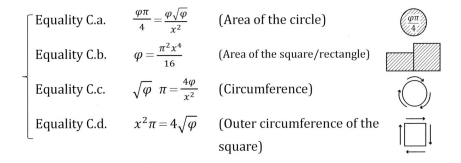

Equality C.a.　$\dfrac{\varphi\pi}{4}=\dfrac{\varphi\sqrt{\varphi}}{x^2}$　　(Area of the circle)

Equality C.b.　$\varphi=\dfrac{\pi^2x^4}{16}$　　(Area of the square/rectangle)

Equality C.c.　$\sqrt{\varphi}\ \pi=\dfrac{4\varphi}{x^2}$　　(Circumference)

Equality C.d.　$x^2\pi=4\sqrt{\varphi}$　　(Outer circumference of the square)

* All the equalities can be calculated based on the equality of A.b.

* When calculating with $\pi\approx3.14$ for reference, $\dfrac{4}{\pi}\approx1.2738$, $\sqrt{\varphi}\approx1.2720$ and $x\approx1.2729$ are obtained and **Figures A, B** and **C** are found to have a "very close value" on one side.

Chapter 3	Deriving $\dfrac{4}{\pi} = \sqrt{\varphi}$ from the Relational Expression

In Chapter 2, the relationship between the circle ratio π and the golden ratio φ was obtained. I would like to find out the relationship between π and φ in this chapter.

For the reader, see **Figures A, B** and **C** and their relational expressions. Did you find anything? ....

I ask you again. Take a little time and look at them again. .....

What! Did you find nothing?

> You may be distracted by the unknown x. Focus on $\sqrt{\varphi}$.
> How is $\sqrt{\varphi}$ working or how does it work in each equality? ....

See **figure A**. The area of the square is obtained by multiplying the area of the circle inscribed by $\dfrac{4}{\pi}$ (*This was explained on page 10). Multiply it by $\sqrt{\varphi}$, which is very close to $\dfrac{4}{\pi}$. It equals the area of the square in **Figure C**. Then, multiply the area and circumference of the circle in **Figure B** by $\sqrt{\varphi}$. The obtained values equal the area of the square in **Figure A** and the circumference of the square in **Figure C**. When they are multiplied by $\frac{4}{\pi}$, the obtained values equal the area and outer circumference of the square circumscribed to each circle. When they are multiplied by $\sqrt{\varphi}$, the obtained values equal the area and outer circumference of the square in a "different figure".

As x, $\frac{4}{\pi}$ and $\sqrt{\varphi}$ are "very close values", is it just a "coincidence"? Do you wonder why such a "coincidence" occurs?

$\frac{4}{\pi}$ and $\sqrt{\varphi}$ are not "very close values", but may be "exactly the same value"?

It should be noted that when the area and circumference of the circle in **Figure B** is multiplied by $\sqrt{\varphi}$ instead of $\frac{4}{\pi}$, the obtained values equal those of the squares in **Figures A** and **C**, respectively This provides a very important clue to find out the relationship between $\frac{4}{\pi}$ and $\sqrt{\varphi}$. I will reveal this is "necessity", not "coincidence" by verification through calculation. For a clear explanation, see the circle in **Figure B**.

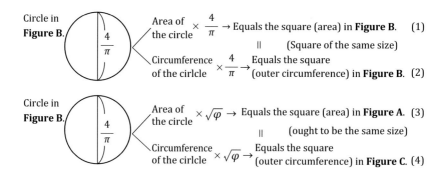

Circle in **Figure B.**

$\dfrac{4}{\pi}$ (4)

Area of the circle $\times \dfrac{4}{\pi} \rightarrow$ Equals the square (area) in **Figure B**. (1)

‖ (Square of the same size)

Circumference of the cirlcle $\times \dfrac{4}{\pi} \rightarrow$ Equals the square (outer circumference) in **Figure B**. (2)

Circle in **Figure B.**

$\dfrac{4}{\pi}$ (4)

Area of the circle $\times \sqrt{\varphi} \rightarrow$ Equals the square (area) in **Figure A**. (3)

‖ (ought to be the same size)

Circumference of the cirlcle $\times \sqrt{\varphi} \rightarrow$ Equals the square (outer circumference) in **Figure C**. (4)

As you can see, when multiplying them by $\sqrt{\varphi}$, which is "very close" to $\dfrac{4}{\pi}$, the obtained values equal those of the squares in **Figures A** and C. Even if it is assumed that they are different from the square in **Figure B** in size, (3) and (4) are supposed to be "the same square in size with different areas and outer circumferences like (1) and (2)" as the same size cirle is multiplied by the same $\sqrt{\varphi}$ (This is a very important point. Do you understand?).

Therefore, I presume that the squares in **Figures A**, and **C** are "the same in size". This means x and $\sqrt{\varphi}$ are equal, and consequently $\sqrt{\varphi}$ and $\dfrac{4}{\pi}$ are equal. As described previously, I will confirm that x, $\sqrt{\varphi}$ and $\dfrac{4}{\pi}$ are equal by verification through calculation. This is because just saying "they ought to be the same size" does not prove that they are so in mathematics.

To verify whether or not $\dfrac{4}{\pi}$ and $\sqrt{\varphi}$ are "exactly the same value", I will assign $\sqrt{\varphi}$ instead of $\dfrac{4}{\pi}$ to the equalities of **Figures A**, **B** and **C**. I will verify this for **Figures A**, **B** and **C** in turn and provide supplemental explanation at the end.

Well, let me start the verification.

Equality of Figure A

When the equality of A.c. in **Figure A** is multiplied by $\frac{4}{\pi}$, the equality of A.d. is obtained. I verify this by multiplying it by $\sqrt{\varphi}$ instead of $\frac{4}{\pi}$ in this process. I compare the two equalities.

$$x\,\pi = \frac{4\sqrt{\varphi}}{x} \xrightarrow{\times \frac{4}{\pi}} 4 \times x = \frac{4\sqrt{\varphi}}{x} \times \frac{4}{\pi} \quad \cdots\cdots\cdots \alpha$$

$(\sqrt{\varphi}$ is multiplied instead$)$

$$x\,\pi = \frac{4\sqrt{\varphi}}{x} \xrightarrow{\times \sqrt{\varphi}} \sqrt{\varphi}\pi \times x = \frac{4\sqrt{\varphi}}{x} \times \sqrt{\varphi} \quad \cdots\cdots\cdots \beta$$

* Numbers are given to differences for easy comparison of the two equalities.

$$(1)\left(\,4\,\right) \times x = \frac{4\sqrt{\varphi}}{x} \times \left(\frac{4}{\pi}\right) (2)$$

$$(3)\left(\sqrt{\varphi}\pi\right) \times x = \frac{4\sqrt{\varphi}}{x} \times \left(\sqrt{\varphi}\right) (4)$$

Both x and $\frac{4\sqrt{\varphi}}{x}$ are equal between the upper and lower equalities. If (1) and (3) , then (2) and (4) are "exactly the same value" then upper and lower equalities α and β are also the same equality.

For reference, I calculate approximate values (1)-(4) again with $\pi \approx$ 3.14 and $\varphi \approx 1.6180$ and show them below.

(1) 4　(2) $\frac{4}{\pi} \approx 1.2738$　(3) $\sqrt{\varphi}\pi \approx 3.9940$　(4) $\sqrt{\varphi} \approx 1.2720$

As you can see, (1) and (3), then (2) and (4) are very close. As $\frac{4}{\pi}$ and $\sqrt{\varphi}$ are very close, this is a natural result.

I will perform the following four calculations to verify whether or not two equalities α and β are the same equality with "exactly the same value".

* Please be careful not to get (1)-(4) wrong in multiplication!

1. Firstly, if (1) and (3), then (2) and (4) are the same, the values obtained by multiplying (1) by (4) and (2) by (3) are equal. Do the math.

$$(4) \times (\sqrt{\varphi}) = (\frac{4}{\pi}) \times (\sqrt{\varphi\pi}) \rightarrow 4\sqrt{\varphi} = 4\sqrt{\varphi} ... \text{They have become equal.}$$
$$(1) \qquad (4) \qquad (2) \qquad (3)$$

2. Secondly, if (1) and (3), then (2) and (4) are the same, the values obtained by assigning (1) instead of (3) and (3) instead of (1) to the equalities, respectively (that is, replacing (1) with (3)) are the same and both values are satisfied. Do the math.

$$\left[\begin{array}{l} \text{Assign (3) to (1)} \quad (\sqrt{\varphi\pi}) \times x = \frac{4\sqrt{\varphi}}{x} \times \frac{4}{\pi} \rightarrow x^2 = \frac{16}{\pi^2} \rightarrow x = \frac{4}{\pi} \\ \text{Assign (1) to (3)} \quad (4) \times x = \frac{4\sqrt{\varphi}}{x} \times \sqrt{\varphi} \rightarrow x^2 = \varphi \rightarrow x = \sqrt{\varphi} \end{array} \right.$$

What! Did you obtain different results?

I confirm whether the two equalities obtained by assignment are different or "the same result" with exactly the same value obtained in two ways. Firstly, see x in **Figure A** again.

x is "one side of the square" and its area x^2 is $\frac{4\sqrt{\varphi}}{\pi}$. A way to satisfy the results of the assignment above is with…

Thinking $x = \frac{4}{\pi} = \sqrt{\varphi}$, $x = \sqrt{\varphi}$ and $x = \frac{4}{\pi}$ are satisfied simultaneously.

Secondly, x is "one side of the square" and the diameter of the circle. The same result as when the area of the circle is calculated is obtained using this. This is the most important and core calculation by which it can be confirmed that $\frac{4}{\pi}$ and $\sqrt{\varphi}$ are the same by calculation. See the following figure. The area of the circle in **Figure A** is $\sqrt{\varphi}$.

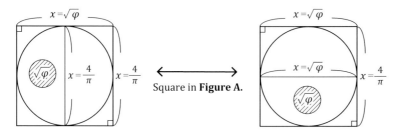

Square in **Figure A.**

(Radius) × (Radius) × π = Area of the circle

$$\frac{2}{\pi} \times \frac{2}{\pi} \times \pi = \sqrt{\varphi}$$

$$\frac{4}{\pi} = \sqrt{\varphi}$$

They are the same result

(Radius) × (Radius) × π = Area of the circle

$$\frac{\sqrt{\varphi}}{2} \times \frac{\sqrt{\varphi}}{2} \times \pi = \sqrt{\varphi}$$

$$\frac{\varphi\pi}{4} = \sqrt{\varphi}$$

$$\frac{4}{\pi} = \sqrt{\varphi}$$

* This proves $\frac{4}{\pi}$ and $\sqrt{\varphi}$ are exactly the same value
* This means the same result is obtained even when (1) and (3) are replaced.

Even if either $\frac{4}{\pi}$ or $\sqrt{\varphi}$, which is obtained by replacement, is assigned in the diameter x, the same result is obtained. This satisfies both $x = \sqrt{\varphi}$ and $x = \frac{4}{\pi}$.

∴ $x = \frac{4}{\pi} = \sqrt{\varphi}$ is satisfied (∵ means therefore).

3. Thirdly, assign (2) and (4) to the equalities (that is, replace (2) with (4)) in the same way as in 2.

$$
\left[
\begin{array}{l}
\text{Assign (4) to (2)} \quad 4 \times x = \dfrac{4\sqrt{\varphi}}{x} \times (\sqrt{\varphi}) \quad \rightarrow \quad x^2 = \varphi \quad \rightarrow \quad x = \sqrt{\varphi} \\[3mm]
\text{Assign (2) to (4)} \quad \sqrt{\varphi}\pi \times x = \dfrac{4\sqrt{\varphi}}{x} \times (\dfrac{4}{\pi}) \quad \rightarrow \quad x^2 = \dfrac{16}{\pi^2} \quad \rightarrow \quad x = \dfrac{4}{\pi}
\end{array}
\right.
$$

The same results are obtained. When comparing these with the result in 2., it is found that with replacement by $(\dfrac{4}{\pi})$ and $(\sqrt{\varphi})$, x has been replaced with $\dfrac{4}{\pi}$ and $\sqrt{\varphi}$. This means the two results are the same even if (2) and (4) are replaced.

$$
\therefore \ x = \sqrt{\varphi} = \dfrac{4}{\pi}
$$

Before starting the fourth verification, do you have one question? It is derived from $x^2 = \dfrac{4\sqrt{\varphi}}{\pi}$ in **Figure A.b.**

Why isn't it determined that $x = \dfrac{4}{\pi} = \sqrt{\varphi}$?

If you think so, see the following figures (**Examples 1 and 2**).

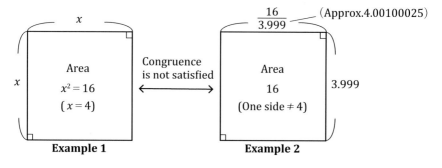

Example 1

Area
$x^2 = 16$
$(x = 4)$

Congruence is not satisfied

$\dfrac{16}{3.999}$ (Approx.4.00100025)

Area
16
(One side $\neq 4$)

3.999

Example 2

Do you understand what the figures mean?   In **Example 1**, one side is 4 and the area is 16.

In **Example 2**, one side is slightly different from 4, but the area is 16, which is the same as that in **Example 1**. As you can see, $x = 3.999 = \frac{16}{3.999}$ is not satisfied.

$x^2 = \frac{4\sqrt{\varphi}}{\pi}$ has been obtained by multiplying the circle with the area $\sqrt{\varphi}$ by $\frac{4}{\pi}$. This means "$x = \frac{4}{\pi} = \sqrt{\varphi}$" cannot be derived without the result that x, $\frac{4}{\pi}$ and $\sqrt{\varphi}$ are equal.

What can be calculated from only $x^2 = \frac{4\sqrt{\varphi}}{\pi}$ is…

$$x = (\frac{4\sqrt{\varphi}}{\pi})^{\frac{1}{2}} \ \text{.....} \ \textbf{Root of} \ \frac{4\sqrt{\varphi}}{\pi} \ (\sqrt{\ \ })$$

Because of this, I proceed with verification in a roundabout way. Well, let's return to the fourth verification.

4. The fourth verification is a calculation that not only I but also you have easily figured out. Like in 1, 2 and 3 above, if (1) and (3), then (2) and (4) are the same, respectively, values obtained by multiplying (1) by (2) and (3) by (4) are supposed to be equal. Do the math.

$$(4) \times (\frac{4}{\pi}) = (\sqrt{\varphi}\pi) \times (\sqrt{\varphi}) \rightarrow \frac{16}{\pi^2} = \varphi \rightarrow \frac{4}{\pi} = \sqrt{\varphi}$$
$$(1) \quad (2) \qquad (3) \qquad (4)$$

The same result was obtained as those of verifications so far. Do you know why this calculation was performed last? In the first verification, it was not clear that $\frac{4}{\pi}$ and $\sqrt{\varphi}$ are "exactly the same value". The verification comes into effect with the second and third verifications.

Then, I complement the four verifications. If x, $\frac{4}{\pi}$ and $\sqrt{\varphi}$ are equal, as to the outer circumferences (squares) in **Figures A, B** and **C**, a value twice the outer circumference $(4x)$ in **Figure A** equals the sum of the outer circumferences in **Figures B** and **C** ($\frac{16}{\pi}$ and $4\sqrt{\varphi}$), $x = \sqrt{\varphi} = \frac{4}{\pi}$ can be derived.

I use the right side of the equality of d. of each figure for calculation.

$$4x \times 2 = \frac{16}{\pi} + 4\sqrt{\varphi} \quad (\frac{32\sqrt{\varphi}}{x\pi} = \frac{4x^2}{\sqrt{\varphi}} + x^2\pi) \leftarrow \text{Right side of the equality is}$$
used

Equality B.a. $\frac{x^2}{\sqrt{\varphi}} = \frac{4}{\pi}$ is assigned $\Big\}$ $\sqrt{\varphi} = \frac{\pi x^2}{4}$ from Equality B.a. is assigned

$$4x \times 2 = \frac{16}{\pi} + 4\sqrt{\varphi} \qquad\qquad 4x \times 2 = \frac{16}{\pi} + 4\sqrt{\varphi}$$

$$2x = \frac{4}{\pi} + \sqrt{\varphi} \qquad\qquad 2x = \frac{4}{\pi} + \sqrt{\varphi}$$

$$2x = \left(\frac{x^2}{\sqrt{\varphi}}\right) + \sqrt{\varphi} \qquad\qquad 2x = \frac{4}{\pi} + \left(\frac{\pi x^2}{4}\right)$$

$$2\sqrt{\varphi}x = x^2 + \varphi \qquad\qquad \frac{8x}{\pi} = \frac{16}{\pi^2} + x^2$$

$$x^2 - 2\sqrt{\varphi}x + \varphi = 0 \qquad\qquad x^2 - \frac{8x}{\pi} + \frac{16}{\pi^2} = 0$$

$$(x - \sqrt{\varphi})^2 = 0 \qquad\qquad (x - \frac{4}{\pi})^2 = 0$$

$$x = \sqrt{\varphi} \qquad\qquad x = \frac{4}{\pi}$$

The same result as those of the four verifications is obtained and $x = \frac{4}{\pi} = \sqrt{\varphi}$ is satisfied.

I can also complement it in another way. I use the equality A.c. $x\pi = \frac{4\sqrt{\varphi}}{x}$ of the circumference in **Figure A**. See the following figures and calculations. $\sqrt{\varphi}$ and $\frac{4}{\pi}$ are like the relationship of "two sides of a coin".

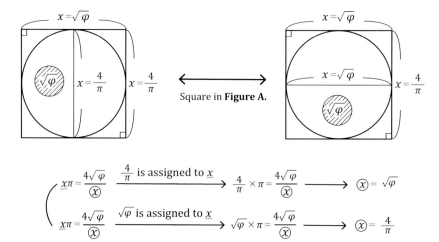

Square in **Figure A.**

$$\left(\begin{array}{l} x\pi = \dfrac{4\sqrt{\varphi}}{\widehat{x}} \quad \xrightarrow{\text{$\frac{4}{\pi}$ is assigned to } \underset{\sim}{x}} \quad \dfrac{4}{\pi} \times \pi = \dfrac{4\sqrt{\varphi}}{\widehat{x}} \quad \longrightarrow \quad \widehat{x} = \sqrt{\varphi} \\[4mm] x\pi = \dfrac{4\sqrt{\varphi}}{\widehat{x}} \quad \xrightarrow{\sqrt{\varphi} \text{ is assigned to } \underset{\sim}{x}} \quad \sqrt{\varphi} \times \pi = \dfrac{4\sqrt{\varphi}}{\widehat{x}} \quad \longrightarrow \quad \widehat{x} = \dfrac{4}{\pi} \end{array} \right.$$

Do you understand the meaning of the calculations? When $\frac{4}{\pi}$ or $\sqrt{\varphi}$ is assigned to one x, another $\widehat{x}$ becomes the opposite $\sqrt{\varphi}$ or $\frac{4}{\pi}$, respectively. That is, it can be confirmed that x is equal to $\frac{4}{\pi}$ and $\sqrt{\varphi}$ simultaneously from the equality of the circumference. The same result is obtained as those of the verifications so far.

$\therefore x = \frac{4}{\pi} = \sqrt{\varphi}$ is satisfied, from which it is found the two equalities α and β are the same equality with "exactly the same value".

Then, I verify it with **Figure B.**

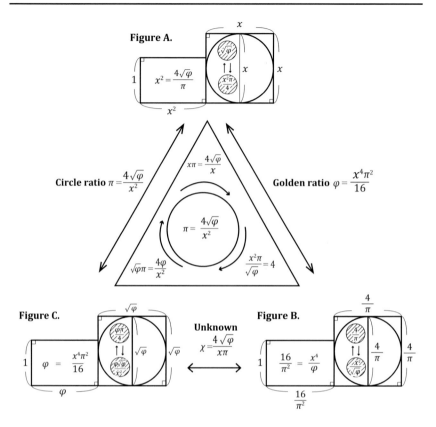

Figure A.

$$x^2 = \frac{4\sqrt{\varphi}}{\pi}$$

$$x\pi = \frac{4\sqrt{\varphi}}{x}$$

Circle ratio $\pi = \dfrac{4\sqrt{\varphi}}{x^2}$

Golden ratio $\varphi = \dfrac{x^4\pi^2}{16}$

$$\pi = \frac{4\sqrt{\varphi}}{x^2}$$

$$\sqrt{\varphi}\pi = \frac{4\varphi}{x^2}$$

$$\frac{x^2\pi}{\sqrt{\varphi}} = 4$$

Figure C.

$$\varphi = \frac{x^4\pi^2}{16}$$

Unknown

$$x = \frac{4\sqrt{\varphi}}{x\pi}$$

Figure B.

$$\frac{16}{\pi^2} = \frac{x^4}{\varphi}$$

Relationship diagram of Unknown $\mathcal{X}$, Golden ratio φ and Circle ratio π

$$\mathcal{X} = \sqrt{\varphi} = \frac{4}{\pi}$$

Figure A. $\cong$ Figure B. $\cong$ Figure C.

Take a little break gazing into the figure above!

Is your brain OK?

Don't you wear a bulldoglike expression?

26

Equality in Figure B.

Though I conduct verification with the same content as in **Figure A**, the explanation is omitted as it is also the same.

In **Figure B**, the equality of B.d. is obtained by multiplying the equality of B.c. by $\frac{4}{\pi}$. In this process, I multiply to verify the equality by $\sqrt{\varphi}$ instead of $\frac{4}{\pi}$. Then, I compare the two equalities.

$$\frac{x^2\pi}{\sqrt{\varphi}} = 4 \xrightarrow{\times\frac{4}{\pi}} \frac{4}{\sqrt{\varphi}} \times x^2 = 4 \times \frac{4}{\pi} \quad \cdots\cdots\cdots \alpha$$

($\sqrt{\varphi}$ is multiplied instead)

$$\frac{x^2\pi}{\sqrt{\varphi}} = 4 \xrightarrow{\times\sqrt{\varphi}} \pi \times x^2 = 4 \times \sqrt{\varphi} \quad \cdots\cdots\cdots \beta$$

* Numbers are given to differences for easy comparison of the two equalities.

$$(1)\left(\frac{4}{\sqrt{\varphi}}\right) \times x^2 = 4 \times \left(\frac{4}{\pi}\right)(2)$$

$$(3)\left(\pi\right) \times x^2 = 4 \times \left(\sqrt{\varphi}\right)(4)$$

Both x^2 and 4 are equal between the upper and lower equalities. If (1) and (3), then (2) and (4) are "exactly the same value", the upper and lower equalities α and β are also the same equality.

For reference, I calculate approximate values (1)-(4) again with $\pi \approx 3.14$ and $\varphi \approx 1.6180$ and show them below.

(1) $\frac{4}{\sqrt{\varphi}} \approx 3.1446$ (2) $\frac{4}{\pi} \approx 1.2738$ (3) $\pi \approx 3.14$ (4) $\sqrt{\varphi} \approx 1.2720$

As you can see, (1) and (3), then (2) and (4) are very close. Like in **Figure A**, I will perform four calculations to verify whether or not two equalities α and β are the same equality with "exactly the same value".

1. Firstly, if (1) and (3), then (2) and (4) are the same, the values obtained by multiplying (1) by (4) and (2) by (3) are equal. Do the math.

$$(\frac{4}{\sqrt{\varphi}}) \times \sqrt{\varphi} = (\frac{4}{\pi}) \times (\pi) \;\rightarrow\; 4 = 4 \ldots\text{They have become equal.}$$
$$\;(1)\qquad\;(4)\quad\;\;(2)\quad\;\;(3)$$

2. Secondly, if (1) and (3), then (2) and (4) are the same, the values obtained by assigning (3) instead of (1) and (1) instead of (3) to the equalities, respectively (that is, replacing (1) with (3)) are the same. Do the math.

$$\left[\begin{array}{l} \text{Assign (3) to (1)} \quad (\pi) \times x^2 = 4 \times \dfrac{4}{\pi} \;\rightarrow\; x^2 = \dfrac{16}{\pi^2} \rightarrow\; x = \dfrac{4}{\pi} \\[2mm] \text{Assign (1) to (3)} \quad (\dfrac{4}{\sqrt{\varphi}}) \times x^2 = 4 \times \sqrt{\varphi} \;\rightarrow\; x^2 = \varphi \;\rightarrow\; x = \sqrt{\varphi} \end{array}\right.$$

$$\therefore\; x = \frac{4}{\pi} = \sqrt{\varphi}\; \ldots\ldots \text{The same result was obtained as that in } \textbf{Figure A.}$$

3. Thirdly, assign (2) and (4) to the equalities (that is, replace (2) with (4)) in the same way as in 2.

$$\left[\begin{array}{l} \text{Assign (4) to (2)} \quad \dfrac{4}{\sqrt{\varphi}} \times x^2 = 4 \times (\sqrt{\varphi}) \;\rightarrow\; x^2 = \varphi \;\rightarrow\; x = \sqrt{\varphi} \\[2mm] \text{Assign (2) to (4)} \quad \pi \times x^2 = 4 \times (\dfrac{4}{\pi}) \;\rightarrow\; x^2 = \dfrac{16}{\pi^2} \;\rightarrow\; x = \dfrac{4}{\pi} \end{array}\right.$$

$$\therefore\; x = \sqrt{\varphi} = \frac{4}{\pi}\; \ldots\ldots \text{The same result was obtained as that in } \textbf{Figure A.}$$

4. Fourthly, if (1) and (3), then (2) and (4) are the same, the values obtained by multiplying (1) by (2) and (3) by (4) are equal. Do the math.

$$\left(\frac{4}{\sqrt{\varphi}}\right) \times \left(\frac{4}{\pi}\right) = (\pi) \times \left(\sqrt{\varphi}\right) \quad \rightarrow \quad \frac{16}{\sqrt{\varphi}\pi} = \sqrt{\varphi}\pi \quad \rightarrow \quad \frac{4}{\pi} = \sqrt{\varphi}$$

The same result was obtained as that in **Figure A**.

Then, I verify **Figure C** with the same content.

Equality in Figure C.

Though I conduct verification with the same content as in **Figures A** and **B**, I have omitted the explanation as it is also the same.

In **Figure C**, the equality of C.d. is obtained by multiplying the equality of C.c. by $\frac{4}{\pi}$. In this process, I multiply the equality by $\sqrt{\varphi}$ instead of $\frac{4}{\pi}$. Then, compare the two equalities.

$$\sqrt{\varphi}\pi = \frac{4\varphi}{x^2} \xrightarrow{\times \frac{4}{\pi}} 4 \times \sqrt{\varphi} = \frac{4\varphi}{x^2} \times \frac{4}{\pi} \quad \cdots\cdots\cdots\cdots \alpha$$

$$\Downarrow \quad (\sqrt{\varphi} \text{ is multiplied instead})$$

$$\sqrt{\varphi}\pi = \frac{4\varphi}{x^2} \xrightarrow{\times \sqrt{\varphi}} \sqrt{\varphi}\pi \times \sqrt{\varphi} = \frac{4\varphi}{x^2} \times \sqrt{\varphi} \quad \cdots\cdots\cdots \beta$$

* Numbers are given to differences for easy comparison of the two equalities.

$$(1) \left(4 \right) \times \sqrt{\varphi} = \frac{4\varphi}{x^2} \times \left(\frac{4}{\pi}\right) (2)$$

$$(3) \left(\sqrt{\varphi}\pi\right) \times \sqrt{\varphi} = \frac{4\varphi}{x^2} \times \left(\sqrt{\varphi}\right) (4)$$

Both $\sqrt{\varphi}$ and $\frac{4\varphi}{x^2}$ are equal between the upper and lower equalities. If (1) and (3), then (2) and (4) are "exactly the same value", the upper and lower equalities α and β are also the same equality.

For reference, I calculate approximate values (1)-(4) again with $\pi \approx 3.14$ and $\varphi \approx 1.6180$ and show them below.

(1) 4   (2) $\dfrac{4}{\pi} \approx 1.2738$ (3) $\sqrt{\varphi\pi} \approx 3.9940$ (4) $\sqrt{\varphi} \approx 1.2720$

As you can see, (1) and (3), then (2) and (4) are very close. Like in **Figures A** and **B**, I will perform four calculations to verify whether or not the two equalities α and β are the same equality with "exactly the same value".

1. Firstly, if (1) and (3), then (2) and (4) are the same, the values obtained by multiplying (1) by (4) and (2) by (3) are equal. Do the math.

$(4) \times (\sqrt{\varphi}) = (\dfrac{4}{\pi}) \times (\sqrt{\varphi\pi}) \to 4\sqrt{\varphi} = 4\sqrt{\varphi}$... They have become equal.
(1)   (4)   (2)   (3)

2. Secondly, if (1) and (3), then (2) and (4) are the same, the values obtained by assigning (3) instead of (1) and (1) instead of (3) to the equalities, respectively (that is, replacing (1) with (3)) are the same. Do the math.

$$\left[\begin{array}{l} \text{Assign (3) to (1)} \quad (\sqrt{\varphi\pi}) \times \sqrt{\varphi} = \dfrac{4\varphi}{x^2} \times \dfrac{4}{\pi} \to x^2 = \dfrac{16}{\pi^2} \quad \to \quad x = \dfrac{4}{\pi} \\ \text{Assign (1) to (3)} \quad (4) \times \sqrt{\varphi} = \dfrac{4\varphi}{x^2} \times \sqrt{\varphi} \quad \to \quad x^2 = \varphi \quad \to \quad x = \sqrt{\varphi} \end{array} \right.$$

$\therefore x = \dfrac{4}{\pi} = \sqrt{\varphi}$ ...... The same result was obtained as that in

Figures A and **B**.

3. Thirdly, assign (2) and (4) to the equalities (that is, replace (2) with (4)) in the same way as in 2.

$$\left[\begin{array}{l} \text{Assign (4) to (2)} \quad 4 \times \sqrt{\varphi} = \frac{4\varphi}{x^2} \times \left(\sqrt{\varphi}\right) \rightarrow x^2 = \varphi \rightarrow x = \sqrt{\varphi} \\ \text{Assign (2) to (4)} \quad \sqrt{\varphi}\pi \times \sqrt{\varphi} = \frac{4\varphi}{x^2} \times \left(\frac{4}{\pi}\right) \rightarrow x^2 = \frac{16}{\pi^2} \rightarrow x = \frac{4}{\pi} \end{array}\right.$$

$$\therefore \ x = \sqrt{\varphi} = \frac{4}{\pi} \ \text{...... The same result was obtained as that in}$$

Figures A. and B.

4. Fourthly, if (1) and (3), then (2) and (4) are the same, the values obtained by multiplying (1) by (2) and (3) by (4) are equal. Do the math.

$$(4) \times \left(\frac{4}{\pi}\right) = \left(\sqrt{\varphi}\pi\right) \times \left(\sqrt{\varphi}\right) \quad \rightarrow \quad \frac{16}{\pi} = \varphi\pi \quad \rightarrow \quad \frac{4}{\pi} = \sqrt{\varphi}$$

The same result was obtained as that in **Figures A** and **B**.

I compared the equality of d. obtained by multiplying c. (equality of circumference) in **Figures A**, **B** and **C** by $\frac{4}{\pi}$ and that obtained by multiplying it by $\sqrt{\varphi}$. As a result, I showed the two equalities α and β were the same equality with "exactly the same value". I also showed $\sqrt{\varphi}$ and $\frac{4}{\pi}$ were "exactly the same value".

Chapter 4   Confirming $\pi = \dfrac{4}{\sqrt{\varphi}}$

Many of you have already noticed it in the process of calculations so far.

$x = \dfrac{4}{\pi} = \sqrt{\varphi}$ ...... That is, $\pi = \dfrac{4}{\sqrt{\varphi}}$ (Title of this book)

$$\pi = \dfrac{4}{\sqrt{\varphi}}$$ **What a beautiful expression it is!**

I confirm whether or not the result obtained through verification can be applied to **Figures A, B** and **C** simultaneously. It is revealed that "coincidence" described on page 17 is actually "necessity". I confirm $\sqrt{\varphi}$ and $\dfrac{4}{\pi}$ are equal by showing the special feature of $\dfrac{4}{\pi}$ hidden in the figures. Though it can be confirmed in all equalities, I assign $\dfrac{4}{\pi}$ and $\sqrt{\varphi}$ to x in the equality of c. (circumference) of each figure, which seems the best. The expression obtained by assignment is found to be a "very beautiful result". If you love mathematics, confirm for yourself whether or not it is correct .

Equality of **Figure A**.c. $x\pi = \dfrac{4\sqrt{\varphi}}{x}$
$\left[\begin{array}{l}\text{Assign } \dfrac{4}{\pi} \quad \dfrac{4\pi}{\pi} = \dfrac{4\sqrt{\varphi}\pi}{4} \;\rightarrow\; \sqrt{\varphi}\pi = 4 \\[2em] \text{Assign } \sqrt{\varphi} \quad \sqrt{\varphi}\pi = \dfrac{4\sqrt{\varphi}}{\sqrt{\varphi}} \;\rightarrow\; \sqrt{\varphi}\pi = 4\end{array}\right.$

Equality of **Figure B**.c $\dfrac{x^2\pi}{\sqrt{\varphi}} = 4$
$\left[\begin{array}{l}\text{Assign } \dfrac{4}{\pi} \quad \dfrac{16\pi}{\pi^2\sqrt{\varphi}} = 4 \;\rightarrow\; \sqrt{\varphi}\pi = 4 \\[2em] \text{Assign } \sqrt{\varphi} \quad \dfrac{\varphi\pi}{\sqrt{\varphi}} = 4 \;\rightarrow\; \sqrt{\varphi}\pi = 4\end{array}\right.$

Equality of **Figure C**.c. $\sqrt{\varphi}\pi = \dfrac{4\varphi}{x^2}$
$\left[\begin{array}{l}\text{Assign } \dfrac{4}{\pi} \quad \sqrt{\varphi}\pi = \dfrac{4\varphi\pi^2}{16} \;\rightarrow\; \sqrt{\varphi}\pi = 4 \\[2em] \text{Assign } \sqrt{\varphi} \quad \sqrt{\varphi}\pi = \dfrac{4\varphi}{\varphi} \;\rightarrow\; \sqrt{\varphi}\pi = 4\end{array}\right.$

The results are all the same. Do you know what happened? The circumferences of **Figures A**, **B** and **C**, which were made separately, are 4 and all the figures are "congruent figures".

Then, focus on the equality of A.c., which has both sides including x and the following calculation. Explanation on page 25 is available for reference.

Equality of A.c.
$x\,\pi = \dfrac{4\sqrt{\varphi}}{x}$
$\left[\begin{array}{l}\text{Assign } \sqrt{\varphi} \text{ to the left and assign } \dfrac{4}{\pi} \text{ to the} \\ \quad \text{right......} \sqrt{\varphi}\,\pi = \sqrt{\varphi}\,\pi \\[1em] \text{Assign } \dfrac{4}{\pi} \text{ to the left and assign } \sqrt{\varphi} \text{ to the} \\ \quad \text{right......} \quad 4 = 4\end{array}\right.$

As $\sqrt{\varphi}\,\pi$ equals 4, the same result is obtained even if $\dfrac{4}{\pi}$ and $\sqrt{\varphi}$ are assigned to left and right x separately and it can be confirmed that $\dfrac{4}{\pi}$ and $\sqrt{\varphi}$ are exactly the same value.

What! Do you want to cofirm it with all the equalities!?

Then, the results of assigning them to all the equalities are shown on the next page.

	Result of assigning $\sqrt{\varphi}$	Result of assigning $\frac{4}{\pi}$	Result of calculating π
Equality of A.a. (Area of the circle)	$\sqrt{\varphi}=\dfrac{4}{\pi}$	$\sqrt{\varphi}=\dfrac{4}{\pi}$	$\pi=\dfrac{4}{\sqrt{\varphi}}$
Equality of A.b. (Area of the square and rectangle)	$\varphi=\dfrac{4\sqrt{\varphi}}{\pi}\left(\dfrac{4\sqrt{\varphi}}{\pi}=\dfrac{16}{\pi^2}\right)$	$\dfrac{16}{\pi^2}=\dfrac{4\sqrt{\varphi}}{\pi}=\dfrac{16}{\pi^2}\,(=\varphi)$	$\pi=\dfrac{4}{\sqrt{\varphi}}$
Equality of A.c. (Circumference)	$\sqrt{\varphi}\,\pi=4$	$\sqrt{\varphi}\,\pi=4$	$\pi=\dfrac{4}{\sqrt{\varphi}}$
Equality of A.d. (Outer circumference of the square)	$\dfrac{16}{\pi}=4\sqrt{\varphi}$	$\dfrac{16}{\pi}=4\sqrt{\varphi}$	$\pi=\dfrac{4}{\sqrt{\varphi}}$
Equality of B.a. (Area of the circle)	$\sqrt{\varphi}=\dfrac{4}{\pi}$	$\sqrt{\varphi}=\dfrac{4}{\pi}$	$\pi=\dfrac{4}{\sqrt{\varphi}}$
Equality of B.b. (Area of the square and rectangle)	$\varphi=\dfrac{16}{\pi^2}$	$\varphi=\dfrac{16}{\pi^2}$	$\pi=\dfrac{4}{\sqrt{\varphi}}$
Equality of B.c. (Circumference)	$\sqrt{\varphi}\,\pi=4$	$\sqrt{\varphi}\,\pi=4$	$\pi=\dfrac{4}{\sqrt{\varphi}}$
Equality of B.d. (Outer circumference of the square)	$\dfrac{16}{\pi}=4\sqrt{\varphi}$	$\dfrac{16}{\pi}=4\sqrt{\varphi}$	$\pi=\dfrac{4}{\sqrt{\varphi}}$
Equality of C.a. (Area of the circle)	$\sqrt{\varphi}=\dfrac{4}{\pi}$	$\sqrt{\varphi}=\dfrac{4}{\pi}$	$\pi=\dfrac{4}{\sqrt{\varphi}}$
Equality of C.b. (Area of the square and rectangle)	$\varphi=\dfrac{16}{\pi^2}$	$\varphi=\dfrac{16}{\pi^2}$	$\pi=\dfrac{4}{\sqrt{\varphi}}$
Equality of C.c. (Circumference)	$\sqrt{\varphi}\,\pi=4$	$\sqrt{\varphi}\,\pi=4$	$\pi=\dfrac{4}{\sqrt{\varphi}}$
Equality of C.d. (Outer circumference of the square)	$\varphi\pi=\dfrac{16}{\pi}=4\sqrt{\varphi}$	$\dfrac{16}{\pi}=4\sqrt{\varphi}$	$\pi=\dfrac{4}{\sqrt{\varphi}}$

To make the results easy to compare, the same expressions are arranged to the left or right of the equalities. From all the equalities, **Figures A**, **B**. and **C**. are congruent and from their equalities we can derive the result of the calculation of $\pi=\dfrac{4}{\sqrt{\varphi}}$.

Now, please look at the "third reason" that wasn't explained completely on page 11 in the table on the next page. You can confirm the very special feature of $\dfrac{4}{\pi}$.

Focus on the undulating-line part of $\dfrac{4}{\pi}$.

Schematic view	Diameter	Circumference	Area of circle	Area of square	Area of four corners		Area of small rectangle	
	$\dfrac{7}{\pi}$	7	$\dfrac{49}{4\pi}$	$\dfrac{49}{\pi^2}$	$\dfrac{49}{\pi^2}$	$-\dfrac{49}{4\pi}$	$\dfrac{49}{\pi^2}$	$-\dfrac{7}{\pi}$
	$\dfrac{6}{\pi}$	6	$\dfrac{9}{\pi}$	$\dfrac{36}{\pi^2}$	$\dfrac{36}{\pi^2}$	$-\dfrac{9}{\pi}$	$\dfrac{36}{\pi^2}$	$-\dfrac{6}{\pi}$
	$\dfrac{5}{\pi}$	5	$\dfrac{25}{4\pi}$	$\dfrac{25}{\pi^2}$	$\dfrac{25}{\pi^2}$	$-\dfrac{25}{4\pi}$	$\dfrac{25}{\pi^2}$	$-\dfrac{5}{\pi}$
	$\dfrac{4}{\pi}$	4	$\dfrac{4}{\pi}$	$\dfrac{16}{\pi^2}$	$\dfrac{16}{\pi^2}$	$-\dfrac{4}{\pi}$	$\dfrac{16}{\pi^2}$	$-\dfrac{4}{\pi}$
	1	π	$\dfrac{\pi}{4}$	1	1	$-\dfrac{\pi}{4}$	0	
	$\dfrac{3}{\pi}$	3	$\dfrac{9}{4\pi}$	$\dfrac{9}{\pi^2}$	$\dfrac{9}{\pi^2}$	$-\dfrac{9}{4\pi}$	$\dfrac{9}{\pi^2}$	$-\dfrac{27}{\pi^3}$
	$\dfrac{2}{\pi}$	2	$\dfrac{1}{\pi}$	$\dfrac{4}{\pi^2}$	$\dfrac{4}{\pi^2}$	$-\dfrac{1}{\pi}$	$\dfrac{4}{\pi^2}$	$-\dfrac{8}{\pi^3}$
	$\dfrac{1}{\pi}$	1	$\dfrac{1}{4\pi}$	$\dfrac{1}{\pi^2}$	$\dfrac{1}{\pi^2}$	$-\dfrac{1}{4\pi}$	$\dfrac{1}{\pi^2}$	$-\dfrac{1}{\pi^3}$

* The reduction scales in the figures are inaccurate.

* Note that "the diamter and area of the circle" and "the area of the four corners and that of the small rectangle" don't become equal in cases where the diameter is not $\dfrac{4}{\pi}$ (However, only if one side of the rectangle is 1 as shown in the figure).

$\frac{4}{\pi}$ has the diameter and area of a circle which are equal. The area of the four corners and that of the small rectangle become equal as shown in the table. This is not seen in a figure that has other diameters.

This special feature is one of the major reasons why I guessed $\frac{4}{\pi}$ and $\sqrt{\varphi}$ are "exactly the same value" (*Note that this is applied only when the left side of the rectangle is 1 like in the figure).

See the following two figures to confirm it.

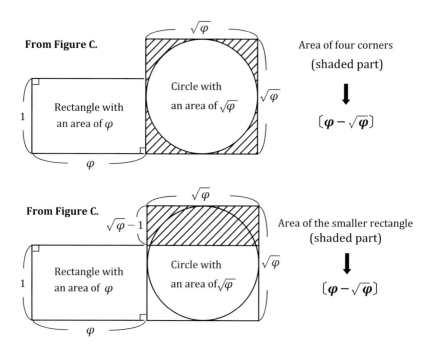

From Figure C.

Rectangle with an area of φ

$\sqrt{\varphi}$

Circle with an area of $\sqrt{\varphi}$

$\sqrt{\varphi}$

1

φ

Area of four corners (shaded part)

↓

$[\boldsymbol{\varphi} - \sqrt{\boldsymbol{\varphi}}]$

From Figure C.

$\sqrt{\varphi} - 1$

Rectangle with an area of φ

$\sqrt{\varphi}$

Circle with an area of $\sqrt{\varphi}$

$\sqrt{\varphi}$

1

φ

Area of the smaller rectangle (shaded part)

↓

$[\boldsymbol{\varphi} - \sqrt{\boldsymbol{\varphi}}]$

It is understood the area of the circle in Figure C. is $\sqrt{\varphi}$ through the verifications so far. From the figures, it is understood the areas of the two shaded parts are $[\varphi - \sqrt{\varphi}]$. Like $\dfrac{4}{\pi}$, the diameter and the area of the circle are equal, the area of the four corners and that of the small rectangle become equal and $\sqrt{\varphi}$ satisfies the special feature only $\dfrac{4}{\pi}$ should have.

From here on, you should understand why the area of the circle was set to $\sqrt{\varphi}$ in the "second reason" on page 13. Proving x is $\sqrt{\varphi}$ leads to proving $\dfrac{4}{\pi}$ equals $\sqrt{\varphi}$. Do you understand why I wrote "If you are a middle school student, don't cheat on an exam!"?

Thank you for reading this book............

What! I will be in trouble if it is over!

The true objective of this book is described later. Many people (including myself and the readers) may not have thought about it. However, this book was written to cast such a large question.

At the end of Chapter 4 we have shown four important relationship diagram of the next.

Relationship diagram between triangle
With golden ratio and each figure I

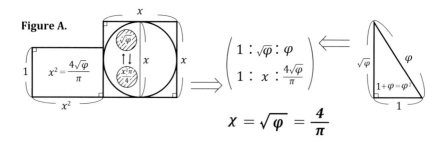

Figure A.

$$x^2 = \frac{4\sqrt{\varphi}}{\pi}$$

$$\left(\begin{array}{c} 1 : \sqrt{\varphi} : \varphi \\ 1 : x : \dfrac{4\sqrt{\varphi}}{\pi} \end{array} \right) \Longleftarrow$$

$$x = \sqrt{\varphi} = \frac{4}{\pi}$$

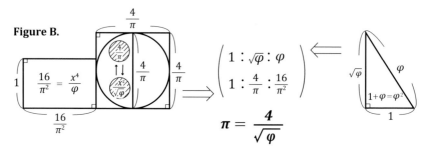

Figure B.

$$\frac{16}{\pi^2} = \frac{x^4}{\varphi}$$

$$\left(\begin{array}{c} 1 : \sqrt{\varphi} : \varphi \\ 1 : \dfrac{4}{\pi} : \dfrac{16}{\pi^2} \end{array} \right) \Longleftarrow$$

$$\pi = \frac{4}{\sqrt{\varphi}}$$

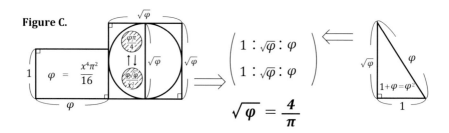

Figure C.

$$\varphi = \frac{x^4\pi^2}{16}$$

$$\left(\begin{array}{c} 1 : \sqrt{\varphi} : \varphi \\ 1 : \sqrt{\varphi} : \varphi \end{array} \right) \Longleftarrow$$

$$\sqrt{\varphi} = \frac{4}{\pi}$$

$$x = \sqrt{\varphi} = \frac{4}{\pi}$$

Note
[:] This mathematical
symbol means ratio in Japan

Figure A. $\cong$ Figure B. $\cong$ Figure C.

©Umeniuguisu 2018, Printed in Japan

Relationship diagram between triangle
With golden ratio and each figure Ⅱ

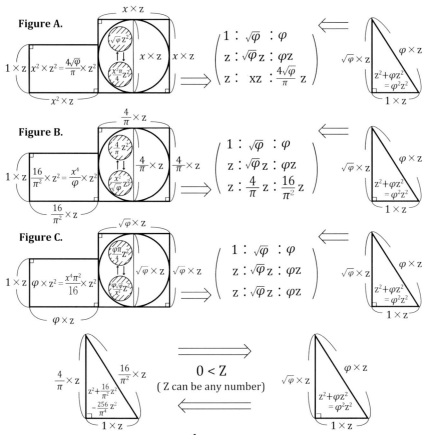

You can check $\pi = \dfrac{4}{\sqrt{\varphi}}$ regardless of the size of Z.

$$\chi Z = \sqrt{\varphi}\, Z = \dfrac{4}{\pi}\, Z$$

Figure A. $\cong$ Figure B. $\cong$ Figure C.

Relationship diagram between triangle
With golden ratio and each figure Ⅲ

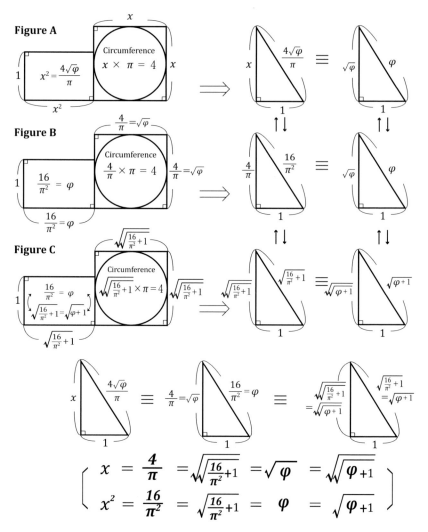

$$\left\{ \begin{array}{l} x = \dfrac{4}{\pi} = \sqrt{\dfrac{16}{\pi^2}+1} = \sqrt{\varphi} = \sqrt{\varphi+1} \\[2mm] x^2 = \dfrac{16}{\pi^2} = \sqrt{\dfrac{16}{\pi^2}+1} = \varphi = \sqrt{\varphi+1} \end{array} \right.$$

Figure A. ≅ Figure B. ≅ Figure C.

Related values of π and φ in the figure

From Figure A. B. C.

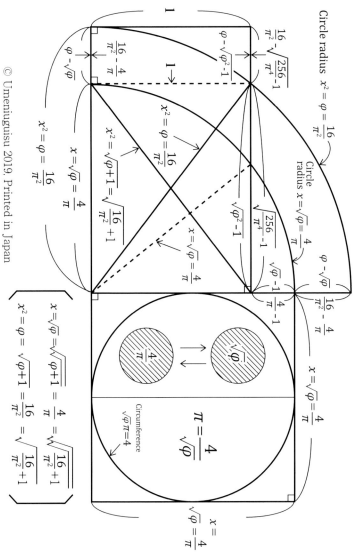

At the end of this book

Did you enjoy reading "Proposal of a new method for calculating π available at the middle school level"? I have something to ask you.

The title of this book......

What!! $\pi = \dfrac{4}{\sqrt{\varphi}}$ Is this true!?

Do you understand "what this really means"? Mathematicians and people familiar with mathematics may have already understood it. I will show it with the following numbers for those who have not noticed.

Currently used π $\pi = 3.14159265358......$

π verified in this book $\pi = 3.14460551102......$

Do you understand what happned?......

As far as I remember, π currently used worldwide was 20 trillion digits in 2016. It seems it was calculated by "supercomputers". The "supercomputer" I bought at 680 yen (tax excluded) at a home center can calculate only up to 12 digits. However many digits can be calculated, there is only one correct value of π.

How do you deal with the differences of there two values?

This is also a question I asked myself. My answer to this question is writing this book.

Finally again, I am neither a mathematician, scientist nor an engineer of a company. I am just an artisan who engages in manual labor in Japan. I leave the authenticity of $\pi = \dfrac{4}{\sqrt{\varphi}}$ to mathematicians and people familiar with mathematics. There is a method of checking the authenticity easily for people less familiar with mathematics including me.

It is……

"Actually measuring"!

This can be aimed at both mathematics professionals and laypeople. It is only accurately measuring. No one can contradict the result of actual measurement. If you are a middle or high school student, how about (extremely accurately) drawing a circle with a diameter of 10m on the floor of the gymnasium and actually measuring its circumference? Or, how about drawing a circle with a diameter of 50m or 100m on a large ground and actually measuring its circumference?

Circle with a diameter of 10m

⌐ The actual measured value is 31m and 41.5 cm
→ Equals currently used π
∟ The actual measured value is 31m and 44.6 cm
→ Equals π of $\dfrac{4}{\sqrt{\varphi}}$

They can be clarified by measuring an actual circle.

An error of approximately 3.1cm in a circle of 10m causes no trouble for common people to have a regular life. However, focus on space.

For the flight distance of an artificial satellite which circles the Earth 300km above (assuming the diameter of the Earth is approx.. 12,700km), a calculation error becomes approx. 39km (An error is 39km!). For example, people on the Earth make a large spaceship and fly into space in the future. The diameter of the galaxy we live in is estimated to be 100,000 light years in diameter.When they circle the galaxy on the spaceship, an error becomes approx.. 310 light years. An error of 310 light years occurs at the speed of light (it can circle the Earth seven and a half times in one second). "Error" is too light a term to express this.

If you have questions or otherwise have an interest in this book, or you are a curious middle or high school student, how about confirming it by actual measurement? If the actual value of the circumference of a circle with a diameter of 10m is 31m and 41.5cm, you can easily prove this book is wrong.

What! Don't I actually measure it?

I have hated drawing circles since I was in kindergarten. If I make a circle, I will fall over with my head spinning. Therefore, I hope someone will confirm the authenticity.

September 27, 2017
Umeniuguisu

BookWay
本とあなたをつなぐ道 ブックウェイ

What!! $\pi=\dfrac{4}{\sqrt{\varphi}}$=3.1446... Is this true!?
[Third edition]

Published in Japan.   ISBN978-4-86584-459-7

Translation from Japanese : GLOVA Corporation
For information contact : BookWay
ONO KOUSOKU INSATSU CO.,LTD.
62, HIRANO-MACHI, HIMEJI-CITY, HYOGO 670-0933 JAPAN
(Phone) 079-222-5372 (Fax) 079-244-1482